Jonny Duddle's

PIRATES

COLOURING BOOK

TREASURE ISLAND
Captain Purplebeard and his pirate crew are looking for a treasure island. Colour in this island to help them.
MIDAS TOUCH

d your
ame here!

.... ISLAND

Now try making an island of your own in the space below. Use your stickers to help you.

Colour in your own
impressive pirate ship.
What will you call her?

MONSTER ISLAND

The pirates have landed on a desert island.
Can you complete the picture using your stickers?
Why not add some palm trees and parrots?

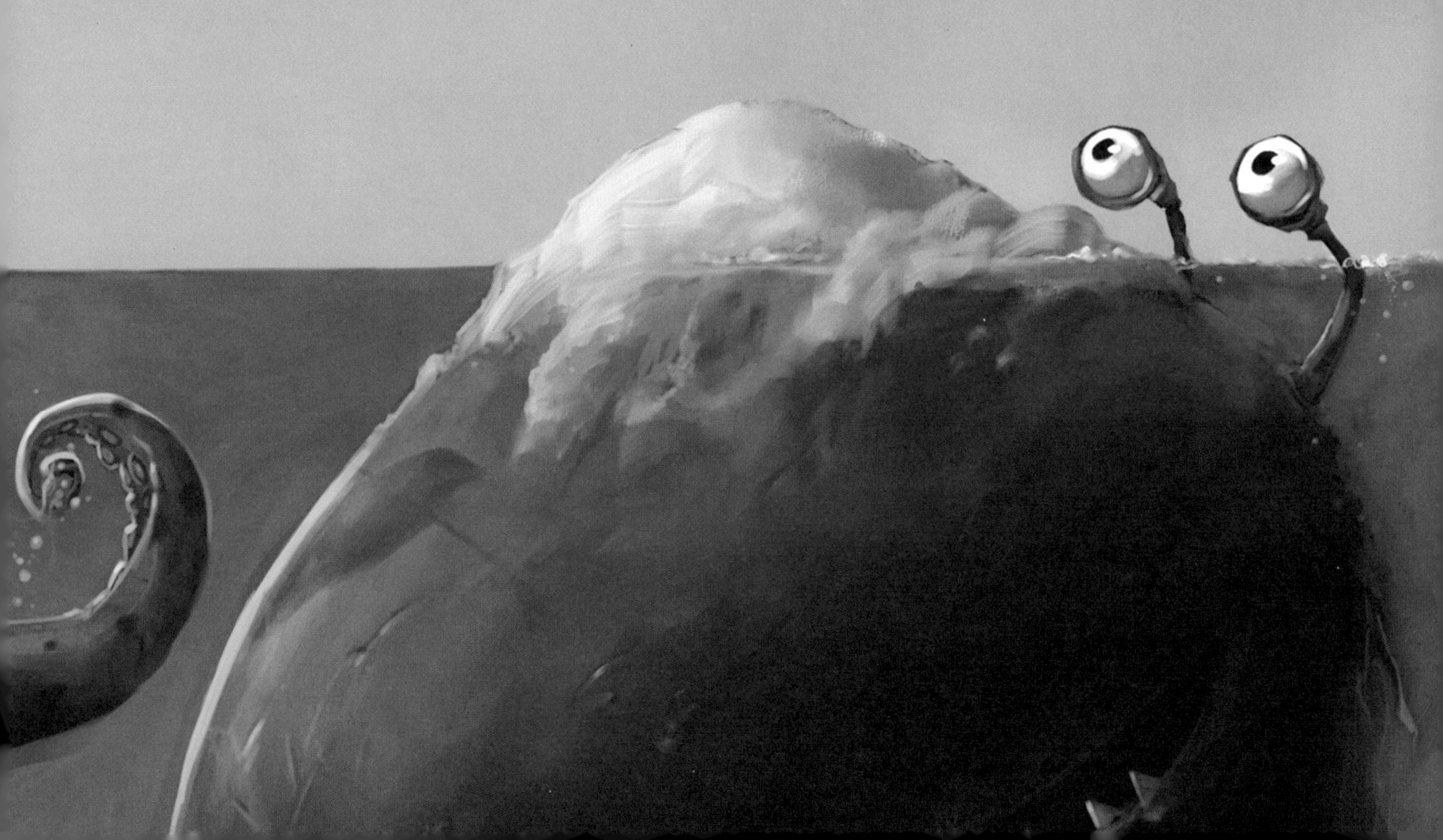

YE OLDE MAP
Can you help Jim Lad to finish his map? Colour it in and add some stickers!

Add a big X to mark the spot
where buried treasure lies!

The crew are dreaming
of treasure. Colour in the
drawings, then fill the
empty thought bubbles
with some treasure
you dream up.

CAPTAIN PURPLEBEARD
What's Captain Purplebeard dreaming about? Scurvy?
Sea monsters? Connect the dots to find out.

SALTY PIRATE STYLE!

The crew need proper pirate outfits!
Join the dots and colour them in.

Sea Monster Gallery
Colour in the fearsome sea creatures!

.... MONSTER

Now invent your own
marine monster above!

Crunch!

Something has caught the greedy pirates! Join the dots, colour in and use your stickers to show what it is.

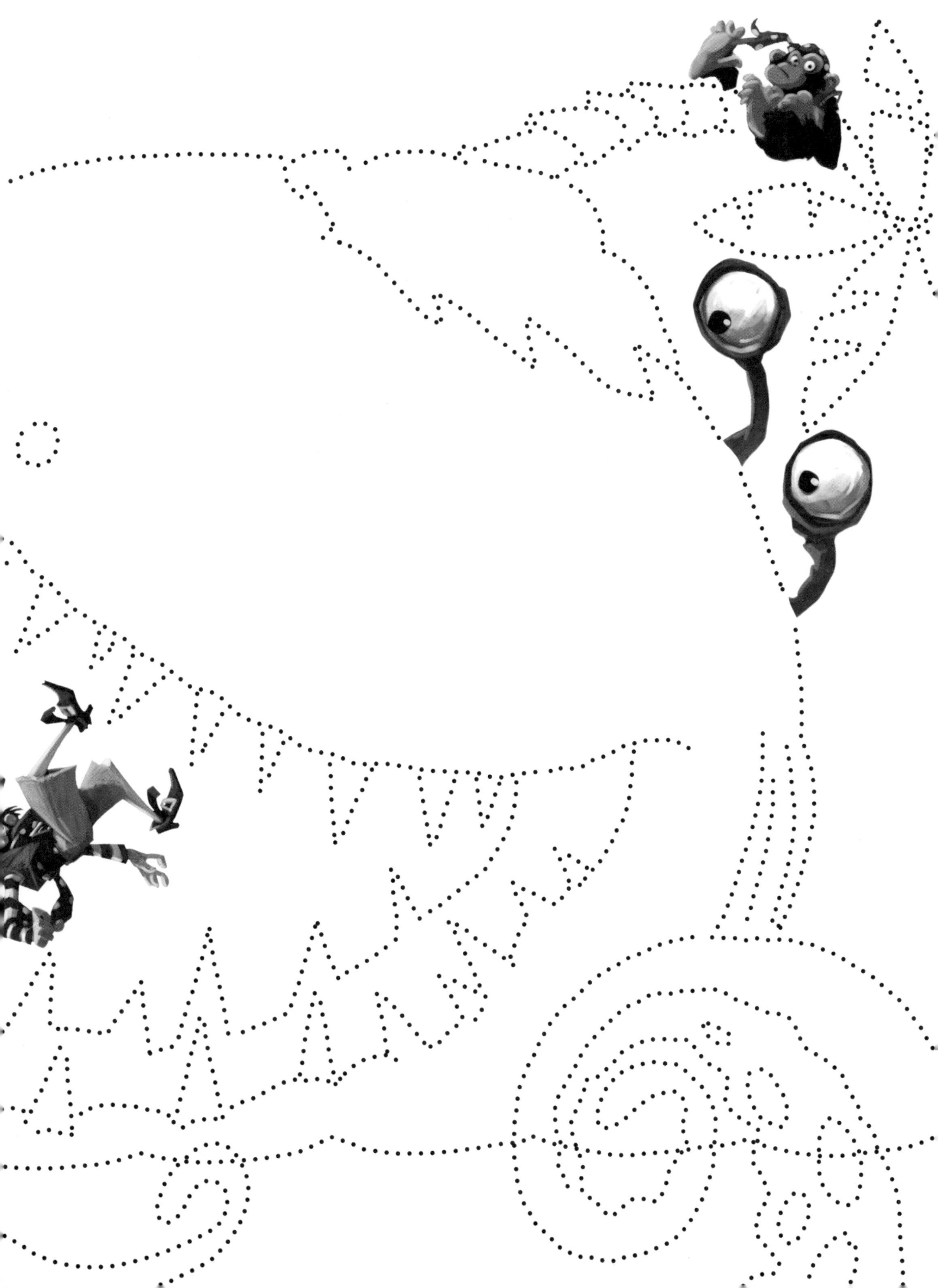

A TEMPLAR BOOK

First published in the UK in 2013 by Templar Publishing,
an imprint of The Templar Company Limited,
Deepdene Lodge, Deepdene Avenue, Dorking, Surrey, RH5 4AT, UK
www.templarco.co.uk

Based on the best-selling picture books *The Pirate-Cruncher*
and *The Pirates Next Door* by Jonny Duddle

1 3 5 7 9 10 8 6 4 2
0113 007

ISBN 978-1-84877-507-7

Designed by Manhar Chauhan and Jonathan Lambert

Printed in Malaysia